Sa nuit d'été (*Its summer night*)

Si je pourrais avec mes mains brûlantes
fondre ton corps autour ton coeur d'amante,
ah que la nuit deviendrait transparente
le prenant pour un astre attardé
qui toujours dès le premier temps des mondes
était perdu et qui commence sa ronde
et tâtonnant de la lumière blonde
sa première nuit, sa nuit, sa nuit d'été.

If, with my burning hands, I could
the body surrounding your lover's
ah! how the night would become t
taking it for a late star,
which, from the first moments of
was forever lost, and which begins iis co....
with its blonde light, trying to reach out towards
its first night, its night, its summer night.

Rainer Maria Rilke

Translated by Byron Adams

Soneto de la noche (*Sonnet of the night*)

Cuando yo muero[†] quiero tus manos en mis ojos:
quiero la luz y el trigo de tus manos amadas
pasar una vez más sobre mí su frescura:
sentir la suavidad que cambió mi destino.

When I die, I want your hands upon my eyes:
I want the light and the wheat of your beloved hands
to pass their freshness over me one more time:
I want to feel the gentleness that changed my destiny.

Quiero que vivas mientras yo, dormido, te espero,
quiero que tus oídos sigan oyendo el viento,
que huelas el aroma del mar que amamos juntos
y que sigas pisando la arena que pisamos.

I want you to live while I wait for you, asleep,
I want your ears to still hear the wind,
I want you to smell the scent of the sea we both loved,
and to continue walking on the sand we walked on.

Quiero que lo que amo siga vivo
y a ti te amé y canté sobre todas las cosas,
por eso sigue tú floreciendo, florida,

I want all that I love to keep on living,
and you whom I loved and sang above all things
to keep flowering into full bloom,

para que alcances todo lo que mi amor te ordena,
para que se pasee mi sombra por tu pelo,
para que así conozcan la razón de mi canto.

so that you can touch all that my love provides you,
so that my shadow may pass over your hair,
so that all may know the reason for my song.

Pablo Neruda

Translated by Nicholas Lauridsen

Soneto LXXXIX *from* 'Cien Sonetos de Amor'
Administered in the U.S. by SADAIC (o/b/o SCD Chile)

[†]Neruda specifically writes 'muero' instead of
the customary 'muera'

Sure on this shining night

Sure on this shining night
Of starmade shadows round,
Kindness must watch for me
This side the ground.

The late year lies down the north.
All is healed, all is health.
High summer holds the earth.
Hearts all whole.

Sure on this shining night
I weep for wonder
Wandering far alone
Of shadows on the stars.

James Agee

Epilogue – Voici le soir (*Night has come*)

Voici le soir;
pendant tout un jour encore je vous ai beaucoup aimées,
collines émues.
C'est beau de voir,
Mais: de sentir à la doublure des paupières fermées
La douceur d'avoir vu …

Night has come;
for one whole day again I've loved you so much,
stirring hills.
It's beautiful to see,
But: to feel in the lining of closed eyelids
the sweetness of having seen …

Rainer Maria Rilke

Translated by Morten Lauridsen

Sa nuit d'été

Rainer Maria Rilke

MORTEN LAURIDSEN

B.2 bar 43–7: omit the low C♯s if out of range.

When performed as a cycle, the piano's final sustaining pedal should connect to, and then be released on, the choir's downbeat rest at the beginning of *Soneto de la noche*. There should be no break between movements.

(c.3')

Soneto de la noche

Pablo Neruda

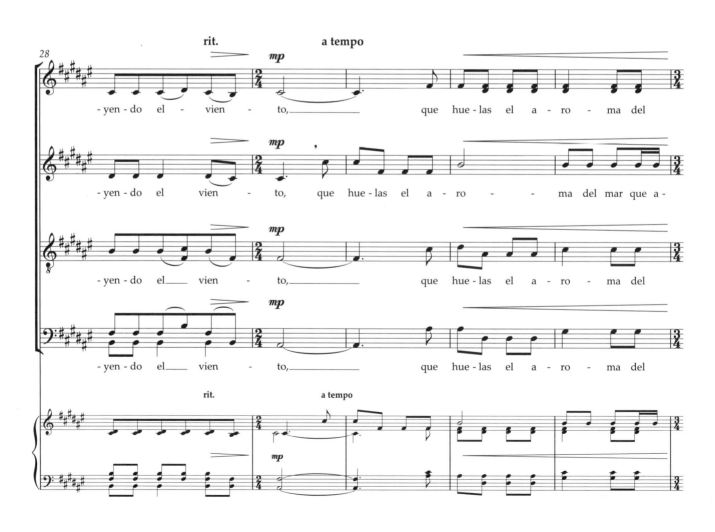

14

16

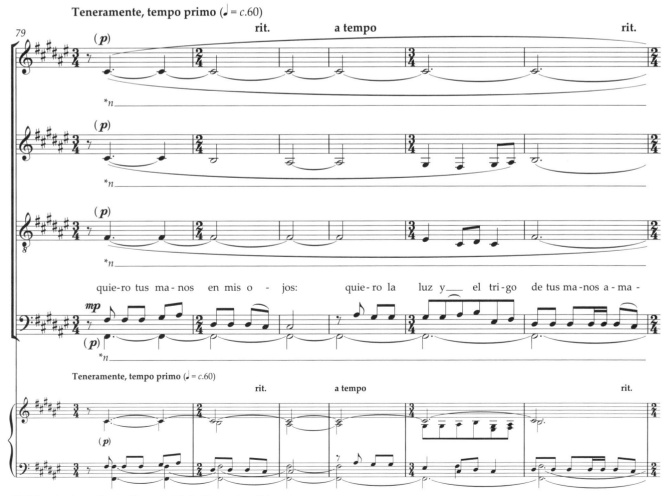

*"*n*" denotes humming on the sound "n". Stagger breathing.

18

mien-tras yo, dor-mi - do, quie-ro que tus oí-dos si-gan o-yen-do el vien -

te es-pe - ro.

que hue-las el a-ro - - ma del mar que a-ma - mos jun-tos
-to, que hue-las el a-ro - ma del mar que a-ma-mos jun-tos
que hue-las el a-ro - ma del mar que a-ma-mos jun-tos
que hue-las el a-ro - ma del mar que a-ma-mos jun-tos

When performed as a cycle, the piano should begin *Sure on this shining night* with the release of the final chord of *Soneto de la noche* in the chorus. There should be no break between movements.

Sure on this shining night

James Agee

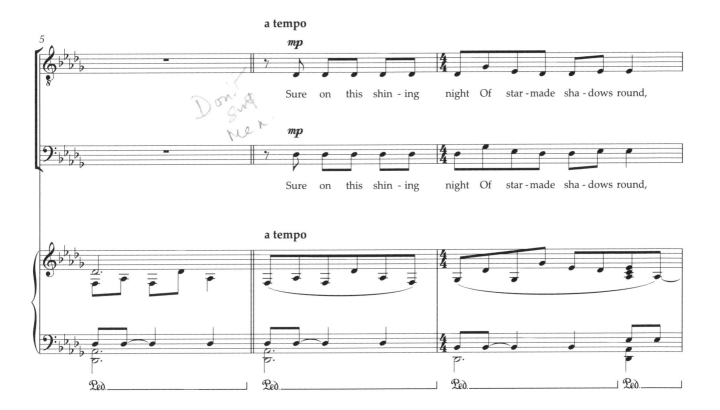

22

*Omit if the low A♭s are out of range.

*Omit if the low A♭s are out of range.

24

-ing night. I weep for won-der Wan-d'ring far a - lone___ Of

-ing night. I weep___ a - lone___ Of

-ing night. I weep for won-der Wan-d'ring far a - lone___ Of

-ing night. I weep___ a - lone___ Of

sha - dows on___ the stars.___ Sure on this

sha - dows on the stars.___

sha - dows on the stars.___

sha - dows on the stars.___ Sure on this shin - ing

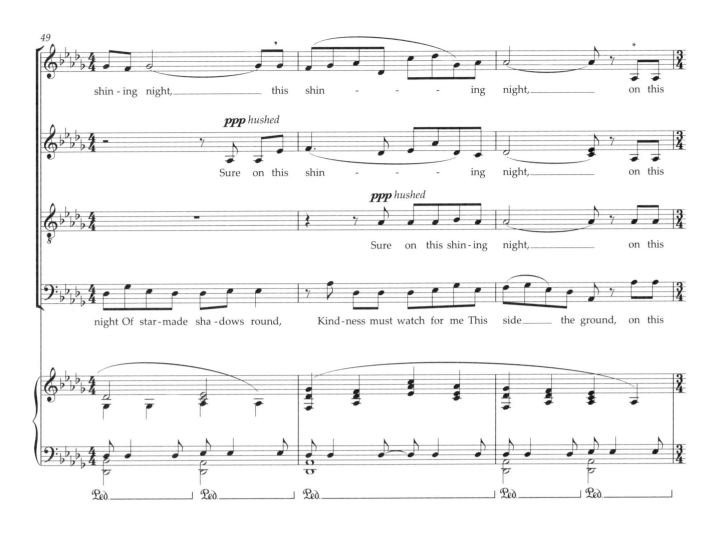

*Omit if the low A♭s are out of range.

(c.4'45")

to Grant Gershon and the Los Angeles Master Chorale

Epilogue – Voici le soir

Rainer Maria Rilke

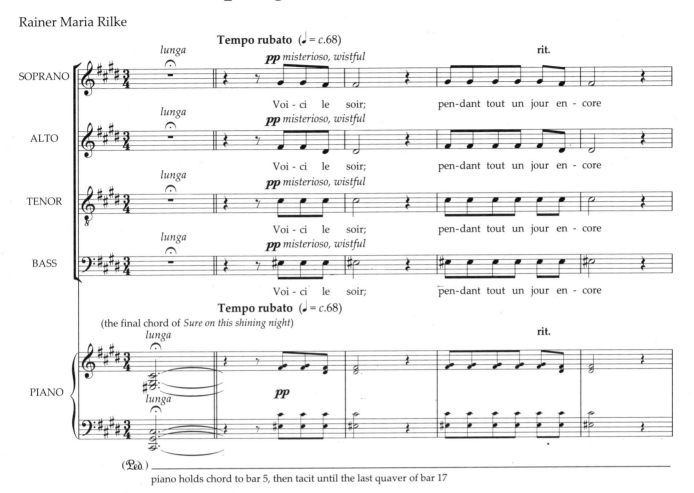

CHORALPROGRAMMESERIES

CONSULTANT EDITOR SIMON HALSEY

SATB / SATB and piano

Nocturnes

Nocturnes addresses aspects of the common theme of 'Night'. Morten Lauridsen's setting of Rilke's impassioned and atmospheric 'Sa nuit d'été' is rich with dense, colourful harmonies, while 'Soneto de la noche' is quiet, serene and folk-like, reflecting the eloquence with which the poet Pablo Neruda speaks of everlasting, eternal love. 'Sure on this shining night' is a lyrical, beautiful setting of James Agee's well loved poem. We return to Rilke in the Epilogue, 'Voici le soir', bringing the Nocturnes to a quiet end as darkness arrives.

The Faber Music Choral Programme Series

The acclaimed Choral Programme Series provides a wealth of invaluable concert repertoire including works by Brahms, Holst, Bridge, Stanford, Warlock, Fauré, Schubert, Saint-Saëns and Schumann, as well as Christmas repertoire, gospel choruses, arrangements of folksongs and hits from the shows.

Also available in this series

Johannes Brahms *Eight romantic partsongs*   SAA acc.: 0-571-51613-0

Benjamin Britten *Three carols*   SA acc.: 0-571-51860-5

Anton Bruckner *Great unaccompanied motets*   SATB acc.: 0-571-51764-1

Gustav Holst *Five partsongs*   SATB acc.: 0-571-51325-5

Morten Lauridsen *Les chansons des roses*   SATB acc.: 0-571-52129-0

Felix Mendelssohn *Four sacred partsongs*   SATB unacc.: 0-571-51363-8

Charles Hubert Parry *Seven partsongs*   SATB unacc.: 0-571-51380-8

Franz Schubert *Three partsongs*   SSAA acc.: 0-571-51309-3

Thomas Tallis *English sacred music*   SATB opt acc.: 0-571-52299-8

Ralph Vaughan Williams *Two partsongs*   SSAATTBB unacc.: 0-571-53036-2

To buy Faber Music publications or to find out about the full range of titles available please contact your local retailer or Faber Music sales enquiries.
Tel: +44 (0)1279 82 89 82   Fax: +44 (0)1279 82 89 83
fabermusic.com   sales@fabermusic.com

ISBN10:   0-571-53382-5
EAN13: 978-0-571-53382-4

ff MUSIC

fabermusic.com

9 780571 533824